Scott, Foresman Reading

On Our Own

Program Authors

Ira E. Aaron
Dauris Jackson
Carole Riggs
Richard G. Smith
Robert J. Tierney

Book Authors

Dauris Jackson
Carole Riggs

Instructional Consultants

John Manning
Dolores Perez

Scott, Foresman and Company
Editorial Offices: Glenview, Illinois

Regional Offices: Palo Alto, California
Tucker, Georgia • Glenview, Illinois
Oakland, New Jersey • Dallas, Texas

CONTENTS

ISBN 0-673-14806-8

Copyright © 1983, 1981,
Scott, Foresman and Company, Glenview, Illinois.
All Rights Reserved.
Printed in the United States of America.

345678910-KPH-9089888786858483

STORIES BY:

Judith Rosenbaum

Wendy Ableman

Duncan Searl

ACKNOWLEDGMENTS

"My Box" from THE WAY THINGS ARE *And Other Poems* by Myra Cohn Livingston (a Margaret K. McElderry Book). Copyright ©1974 by Myra Cohn Livingston. Used by permission of Atheneum Publishers and McIntosh and Otis, Inc.

"Reading" from RHYMES ABOUT US by Marchette Chute. Copyright © 1974 by Marchette Chute. Reprinted by permission of the publisher, E. P. Dutton.

ILLUSTRATIONS

Cover: Norman Green
Margot Apple: pages 70-75; James Dyekman: 58-63; Pamela Baldwin Ford: 19-23; Will Harmuth: 9-13, 48-52; Tien Ho: 38-41, 64-69; Maggie MacGowan: 4-8, 24-27; Anthony Rao: 42, 43-47, 53-57; Christopher Santoro: 14-18, 34-37; George Suyeoka, 28; Jennie Williams: 29-33; Jerry Zimmerman: 76-79.

Studio: *Kaeser and Wilson Design, Ltd.*

Going to See the Animals

We are going to see animals.

Good! I like to look at animals.

Come on.
Come with Mom and me.
We can all go to see the animals.

4

 I like going to the zoo.
What animals are we going to see at
the zoo?

 We are not going to the zoo.

 But I wanted to look at animals.

 We are going to look at animals.
But we are not going to the zoo.

 What animals are not at the zoo?
Look at this shop.
It is not a zoo.
But it has animals.
Are we going to this shop?

 We are not going to a shop.

6

Animals are in books.
Are we going to look at animal books?
I like animal books.

 We are not going to look at books.
But you are going to like the
animals you see.
They are animals you can play with.

This is what we wanted you to see.
It is not a shop.
It is not a zoo.
The animals can come over to you.

I like this.
It is not like a zoo at all.
But it has animals.
It has animals I can play with.

8

Ships in Jars

Look at this ship.
Look at all the sails it has.
It looks like a good sailing ship
to me.

My grandpa makes ships like this.
But the ships my grandpa makes are
all in jars.

Ships in jars?
But ships can't get in jars.

 They can.
Come with me to see my grandpa.
You can see all the ships in jars.

10

This is the house.
And this is my grandpa.
Grandpa, this is Tim.
Tim wants to see a ship get
in a jar.

It is good to see you, Tim.
Come in the house with me.
You are going to see a ship get
in a jar.

11

Look at all the ships you have.
And they are all in jars.

And now this ship is going to go in
a jar.
Look, Tim.
I make the sails go down like this.
Now the ship can get in the jar.

But now it is not like a ship.
I can't see the sails.

12

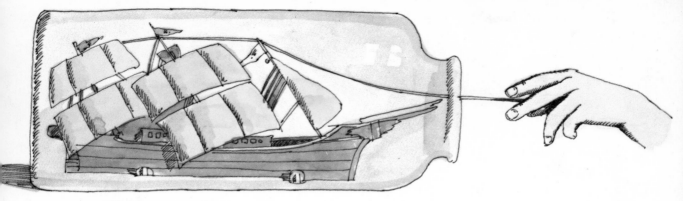

 Look at the ship now, Tim.
Now you can see the sails.

 Look at the ship in the jar.
It looks like a good sailing ship.
Can it sail?

 The ship can't sail, Tim.
But the jar can.

Is That the Animal?

 Would you help me?
I came to find the animal.
Would you help me find the animal
I want?

 You came to a good place.
The zoo is a good place to find animals.
I'll help you look for the animal you
want.

14

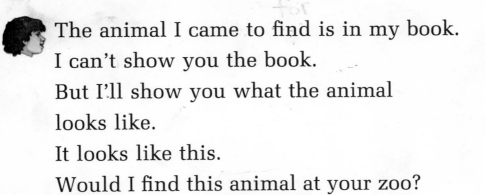

The animal I came to find is in my book.
I can't show you the book.
But I'll show you what the animal
looks like.
It looks like this.
Would I find this animal at your zoo?

I'll show you what we have at this zoo.
I'll help you look for the animal
you want.

Look over there.
Is that the animal you are looking for?
It looks like what you wanted.

That isn't it.
I like that animal over there.
But it isn't the animal I came to find.

16

 Look over there.
Is that the animal you want?

 That isn't it.

 Is that the animal?

 That isn't it.

Look over there!
There is the animal I came to find.
What a good zoo you have.
You have the animal in my book.

 But that's not a zoo animal at all.

 It isn't?

18

What Is It?

Grandma told Jen, "I put something in the mail for you."

Jen said, "Good. I like to get mail. What is it?"

"You are going to find out," said Grandma.

Jen said, "I want to find out now. Is it something to play with? Is it something to put on? Is it a dog?"

Grandma told Jen, "I can't tell you
what it is.
But I can tell you this.
You are going to like it.
I chose it for you.
It is something you want."

Jen looked for the mail.

Jen said, "Mom, has the mail come?
Is there something in it for me?"

Mom told Jen, "The mail came.
And your name is on this box."

Jen said, "That's it!
That's what Grandma put in the mail.
Now I'll see what Grandma
chose for me."

Jen said, "What is all this?
It isn't something to play with.
It isn't something to put on.
But Grandma said I wanted it.
What is in this box that I want?"

Mom told Jen, "You can make a house
with all this.
Dad and I can help you.
The house is going to look like this."

Jen said, "But that is a house for
a dog.
And there isn't a dog to put in it."

Mom told Jen, "There is now.
Look behind you.
This is your new dog.
We chose the dog for you.
And Grandma chose the house."

What Is in the Box?

Ted said, "I like this shop.
This is a good shop to look in."

Lucy said, "Look at this box.
Is something in it?
I would like to see what is in it."

Mr. Vega said, "You can look in it.
Look in the box and see what you find."

Lucy said, "Look at this!
I like what is in this box."

Ted said, "But look. I see a
giant box.
What can go in a giant box like that?
Is a table in it?
Is a house for a dog in it?
Is a giant animal in it?"

Mr. Vega said, "Look in the giant box
and see."

Ted said, "Look! A box is in the
giant box.
And a box is in the box in the
giant box."

Lucy said, "Go on looking.
And I'll help you."

26

Ted said, "Now we have a box and a
box and a box and a box.
And they all go in the giant box.
I like the giant box.
Look at all that can go in it."

"And look at all that comes out,"
said Lucy.

My Box

by Myra Cohn Livingston

Nobody knows what's there but me,
knows where I keep my silver key
and my baseball cards
and my water gun
and my wind-up car that doesn't run,
and a stone I found with a hole clear through
and a blue-jay feather that's <u>mostly</u> blue,
and a note that I wrote to a guy next door
and never gave him—and lot, lots more
of important things that I'll never show
to anyone, <u>anyone</u> else I know.

28

Something for Carmen

Carmen said, "Look! There is
something by my door.
It is a box with birds in it.
What a good thing to get!
But who could have put it by my door?
There isn't a name on it.
I have to find out who put it there."

Carmen said, "I wish I could find
out who put this box by my door.
Milly, did you put a box by my door?
There are good things in the box."

Milly told Carmen, "I did not put
it there.
Did Tom put it there?"

Carmen said, "Who put this box there?
I wish I could find out who did it.
Tom, did you put a box by my door?"

Tom said, "Who, me?
I did not put it there.
Did Milly put it there?"

Carmen said, "I wish I could find out
who put this box by my door.
Tom did not put it there.
Milly did not put it there.
I like the box and the good things
in it.
But who could have put it by my door?"

Carmen said, "Now I see who did it.
Dad makes things like this.
Dad, did you put this box by my door?"

Dad said, "I did.
You helped me make a new table for
the yard.
And I wanted to make something
for you."

"What a dad you are!" said Carmen.

Are They People?

Cat said, "Are you going away, Bear?
Where are you going?"

Bear said, "I want to look for people.
I want to see what people are like."

Cat said, "I can tell you all about
people.
I can show you where they come from."

Bear said, "I would like that."

34

Bear and Cat walked and walked.
First they came to a big yard.

Bear said, "Look over there.
Are they people?"

Cat said, "They are dogs, not people.
I can tell you all about dogs.
Dogs are not at all like people.
Come away, Bear.
We have to go on looking."

Next Bear and Cat came to a big yellow house.

Bear said, "What about this house? Are there people in it?"

Cat said, "This isn't a house for people.
It is a house for birds.
Come away, Bear.
We have to go on looking."

36

At last Bear and Cat came to a big
green place.

Cat said, "Look, Bear.
This is a place where you can find
people.
Look at all the people."

Bear said, "Now I see what people are
like.
I like people.
And I can see that people like bears."

A Book For Brian

"Can you play with me?" said Brian to
Mom.
Mom said, "I can't play now.
But look over there by the yellow box.
That book is for you."

Brian said, "For me?
I like books.
I'll look at it now."

Brian looked at the new book.

Brian said, "What a good book this is!
It has all the things I like in a book.
Look at all it tells about animals.
And it has things for me to make.
I would like to make all the things.
Where did you get this book, Mom?"

Mom laughed and said, "I did not <u>get</u>
the book.
But I can tell you all about it.
Look at what is on the book."

Brian looked at the book.
The book said "By Pam Marks" on it.

Brian said, "But <u>you</u> are Pam Marks!
This book is by you!
Now I see where all the good things in
it come from.
You put all the things I like in your
book.
What a mom you are!
I have a mom who makes books!"

Reading

by Marchette Chute

A story is a special thing.
　　The ones that I have read,
They do not stay inside the books.
　　They stay inside my head.

Wishing

Jake said, "What wish do you have, Meg?
I would like to know what you wish for."

Meg said, "I wish I could sing.
I could sing about all the things
I like.
I could sing about playing and animals
and things like that.
I could sing for all of you."

Jake said, "I am good at singing, Meg.
I'll show you how to sing.
We could sing together.
You can have your wish.
Do you have a wish, Max?"

Max said, "I wish I could make things.
I would like to make animals and
tables and things like that."

44

Jake said, "I know how to make things
like that.
I'll show you how, Max.
You can have your wish.
We could all make things together.
We could make big red houses.
We could make big yellow tables.
We could make a big, big box to put
things in."

Meg said, "We told you what we wished for, Jake.
Now we want to know your wish.
Do you have a wish?
What do you wish for?"

Jake said, "I would like to fly.
I wish we could all fly.
We could fly together over houses and lakes.
We could fly to places where people can't go."

Meg said, "That is a good wish, Jake.
But we can't fly over houses and lakes."

Max said, "But we can do something
that is like flying.
Meg and I can show you how."

Something New to Do

"I wish I could find something to do,"
said Peg.

Mom said, "What about playing with
your animals?"

Peg told her, "I did that.
Now I would like to do something new."

48

Mrs. Pine and Jed came by the house.

"Where are you going?" said Peg.

Jed told her, "We are going to work in the park."

Peg said, "What work can you do there?
People do not work in parks.
Parks are for playing."

Mrs. Pine told Peg, "There is work to
do in parks.
We are going to work on the plants.
Would you like to help?"

Peg said to her, "I wanted something
new to do.
I'll come and work with you."

And Peg came with Jed and Mrs. Pine.

50

"What plants are we going to work on?"
said Peg.

Jed told her, "We are going to work on
the animal plants."

Peg said, "Animal plants?
But animals do not come from plants.
Flowers come from plants.
How can a park have animal plants?"

"You are going to see," said Mrs. Pine.

They all came to the park.

"Look at the plants over there," said
Mrs. Pine.

Peg said, "They look like animals!
I see cat plants and bird plants and
a bear plant.
How do plants get to look like that?"

Jed said, "The plants are cut to look
like animals.
And now you can help.
We can all work on the plants together."

52

Adam Knows It All

Adam said, "I know all there is to know.
I know all about plants and animals.
I know all about people and places.
There isn't a thing I do not know."

Kim said, "You can't know all there is
to know.
My Mom and Dad do not know all that.
Where do you find out about things?
Who tells you?
What book would have all that in it?"

Adam said, "I am good at finding out
about things.
I can't tell you how.
But I know I am good at it."

54

Kim said, "How can you know all that?
Tell me all you know about animals."

Adam said, "I know that animals like
to play.
I know that there are big animals.
And I know that big animals have to
have big houses."

Kim said, "Is that all?
I know all that.
And I know where animals come from.
This animal comes from a cōld place.
This animal comes from a place with
plants all over it.
Did you know that?"

Adam laughed.

"I know it <u>now</u>," Adam said.

Kim said, "Now I know how you find
out about things.
You get people to tell you what they
know."

Kim laughed.

Flying to Rom

Mixi has a flying car.
It can fly to lands that are far away.
It can fly to lands you could not find.

Her friend Moe said, "I want to go flying.
Where can we go?"

Mixi told Moe, "I know where blue comes from.
We can fly there together."

58

Mixi told Moe, "All blue comes from
a big lake of blue light.
This lake is far, far away.
It is in the land of Rom."

Moe said, "I would like to see that
lake."

Mixi and Moe jumped in the flying car.

Together they said, "Get going, car.
Go far, far away."

And the car did what they told it to do.

Mixi and Moe looked out of the car.
First the car came to a land of green cats.
Mixi and Moe could see green cats all over the place.
They could see people playing with the cats.

Moe said, "Is this the land of Rom?"

"It isn't," Mixi told him.

60

Next Mixi and Moe came to a land of
giant plants.
They could see big, big plants all over.

Moe said, "What big plants they are!
Is this the land of Rom?"

Mixi said, "This isn't the land of Rom.
The land of Rom is next.
It is the last place we come to."

At last the car came to the land of Rom.

Mixi told Moe, "Look over there.
Look at that big lake.
Look at the blue light flying out of it.
This is where blue comes from."

Moe looked and looked at the light.

Moe said, "How blue it is!
I like this far land.
And I am glad to know where blue
comes from."

Put It Together

"What are you doing?" said Sam.

Judy told him, "I am going to put
this together.
Would you like to help?"

Sam said, "I would like to help.
What is it going to look like?"

Judy said, "Look on the box.
The box shows what the pieces make."

64

Sam said, "Look at all the pieces in
the box.
I do not know what to do first.
Do you?"

Judy said, "My mom told me what to do.
I'll tell you what Mom said.
First look at the red car on the box.
All the red pieces make the car.
Help me find the red pieces."

Sam said, "There is a red piece.
And there is a red piece.
Now we have all the red pieces."

Judy said, "Good. Now we can make
the car.
Help me put it together."

Sam told Judy, "I know what to do next.
I can show you.
Look at the park behind the car.
The park is all green.
We have to find all the green pieces to
make the park."

Judy said, "Now we have all the green
pieces.
This green piece can go in that plant."

Sam told her, "The plant is light green.
This piece isn't.
This piece is for the flowers behind
the car."

68

Judy said, "Look. Now all we have to
do is this yellow bird.
Find all the yellow pieces for me."

Sam said, "You have all the yellow
pieces."

Judy said, "But look at the bird.
Where is the last yellow piece?"

Sam told her, "I see it.
You are not going to like this.
Rip has the yellow piece.
Now all we have to do is get Rip."

Working and Playing

What work do you do at your house?
I'll show you what we do.
We wash the dishes.
We wash the car.
We wash Pal.
We do not wash Tib at all.
It is not good for Tib to get washed.

Skills Unit 9

Washing is good for dishes.
Washing is good for a car.
Washing is good for Pal.
But washing is not good for Tib.

Mom and Dad have work to do in the house too.

This is Dad working.

Mom and Ray are there too.

Can you see what work Mom and Ray are doing?

Dee is in her house.

Dee is not working.

Mom likes to work on her plants.
Mom is good with plants.
Mom works on her plants behind the house.
Mom is going to show me how to plant flowers.

What do you do for fun?
I'll show you what we do.
Jill and Tib like to play together.
I like to sing.
Dad likes to sing too.
This is Dad singing with Pal.
Pal's singing makes Dee laugh.
Do you like to sing?

74

I like to have fun.
But I like doing my work too.
You know, working together makes
working fun.

Going Away

Joe said, "I want to go to Animal Land.
But Animal Land is far, far away.
How can I get there?"

Deb said, "I can make something to get
you there.
You can help me.
And we can go to Animal Land together."

Deb said, "I have to have a box."

Joe said, "You can have this box.
I wash my dishes in it.
But I do not have to do the washing
now."

Ed said, "How can a box help you get
far, far away?"

Deb said, "I'll show you."

They worked together on the box.
Deb told Joe where to put it.

Deb said, "Now all I have to have is
your door."

Joe said, "How can my door help you?"

Deb said, "I'll show you.
Put the door down like this.
And we can get in the box."

"Now what do we do?" said Joe.

Deb said, "Ed, you can help.
You can help Joe and me go away to
Animal Land.
Jump on the door over there."

"Away we go!" said Joe.

MASTERY WORD LISTS

The following high-frequency words (words that appear on recognized word frequency lists) have been read a minimum of twelve times by the end of this book. Pupils should be able to recognize both the root word and the root word with these endings: s, es, 's, ed, ing.

The page number printed after each word in the first list shows the first appearance in this book. The second list is a cumulative list of previously mastered words.

would	14	said	19	where	34	fly	47
came	14	by	29	people	34	her	48
I'll	14	thing	29	about	34	work	49
that	16	who	29	big	35	land	58
there	16	could	29	do	43	far	58
told	19	wish	30	know	43	wash	70
put	19	did	30	sing	43		
something	19	away	34	together	44		

a	for	light	table
all	get	like	the
and	giant	look	they
animal	girl	make	this
are	go	me	to
at	going	my	under
behind	good	name	want
blue	green	new	we
book	has	not	what
box	have	now	with
boy	help	on	yard
but	house	out	yellow
can	I	over	you
can't	in	play	your
cold	is	red	zoo
come	it	run	
down	jump	see	
find	laugh	shop	